Earth's Endangered Creatures

SAVE THE MACAWS

Written by
Jill Bailey

Illustrated by
Ann Baum

This series is concerned with the world's endangered animals, the reasons why their numbers are diminishing, and the efforts being made to save them from extinction. The author has described these events through the eyes of fictional characters. Although the situations are based on fact, the people and the events described are fictitious.

A Templar Book
First published in Great Britain in 1991
by Heinemann Children's Reference,
a division of Heinemann Educational Books Ltd
Halley Court, Jordan Hill, Oxford OX2 8EJ
Devised and produced by The Templar Company plc
Pippbrook Mill, London Road, Dorking, Surrey RH4 1JE
Copyright © 1991 by The Templar Company plc
Illustrations copyright © 1991 by The Templar Company plc

Picture credits
(*a*=above, *m*=middle, *b*=below)

Cover: *Portraits:* Hutchison Library; *a* Brian Moser, *m* Jesco von Putikemer, *b* Nancy Durrell McKenna
Macaws: Gordan Langsbury/Bruce Coleman Ltd.

Page 5 Gordan Langsbury/Bruce Coleman Ltd; *page 6 a* Brian Moser/Hutchison Library, *b* Erwin and Peggy Bauer/Bruce Coleman Ltd; *page 10* Martin Wendler/Frank Lane Picture Agency; *page 12* Jane Burton/Bruce Coleman Ltd; *page 15* Gunter Ziesler/Bruce Coleman Ltd; *page 16* L.C. Marigo/Bruce Coleman Ltd; *page 17* Gunter Ziesler/Bruce Coleman Ltd; *page 18* L.C. Marigo/Bruce Coleman Ltd; *page 20* Jesco von Putikemer/ Hutchison Library; *page 21* Martin Wendler/Frank Lane; *page 23* J. Cancalosi/Bruce Coleman Ltd; *page 26* Konrad Wothe/Frank Lane; *page 27* Bruce Coleman Ltd; *page 28* Frank Lane; *page 30* Nancy Durrell McKenna/Hutchison Library; *page 31* Jane Burton/ Bruce Coleman Ltd; *page 32* Konrad Wothe/Bruce Coleman Ltd; *page 35 a* Martin Wendler/Frank Lane, *b* Hugh Clark/Frank Lane; *page 36* Rod Williams/Bruce Coleman Ltd; *page 40* Frank Lane; *page 43* Erwin and Peggy Bauer/Bruce Coleman Ltd.

Editor Andy Charman
Designer Philip Hargraves
Picture researcher Jenny Faithful
Consultant Peter Evans

Colour separations by Positive Colour Ltd, Maldon, Essex, Great Britain
Printed and bound by L.E.G.O., Vicenza, Italy

British Library Cataloguing in Publication Data
Bailey, Jill
Macaw.
1. Parrots
I. Title II. Series
598.71
ISBN 0-431-00819-1

CONTENTS

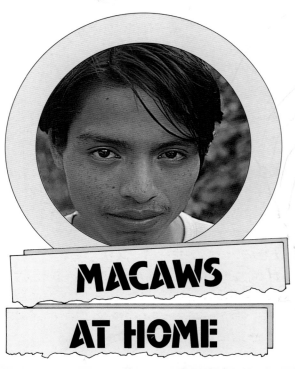

MACAWS AT HOME

There was a sudden rustle of wings and the nearby branches shook. **Hector Hernandez** froze, and turned his head very slowly. A pair of red-and-green macaws had landed in a tree just 5 metres away. Their brilliant plumage glowed in the morning sunlight as it filtered through the branches of the Peruvian rainforest. Hector could hear nuts being broken open. Slowly, he lifted the insect-proof

A blue-and-gold macaw in its forest home. This forest is being cut down to make room for towns and cities.

netting away from his face and raised his binoculars. The macaws were feeding, gripping nuts in one foot while they cracked them with their powerful bills.

The macaws finished their snack, and began to preen each other. Male and female macaws pair for life, and spend a lot of time preening each other's feathers. When birds preen they use their bills to clean and arrange their feathers.

Hector forced himself to turn back to the birds he was supposed to be watching. These were a pair of blue-and-gold macaws that were nesting in a hollow tree trunk below him. Macaws nest in ready-made holes. Hector could just make out the bright blue head of the female as she sat on her eggs.

Soon the male returned. His throat was swollen with food for his mate. Macaws and many other parrots have a large pouch, called a crop, in their throats which they use to store food. The male macaw coughed up, or regurgitated, the food for the female to swallow.

From his harness up in a tree, Hector could see across the top of the forest. The netting with which his head was covered protected him from biting insects.

There was a crackle from the walkie-talkie radio strapped to Hector's waist. It was Pedro, a Brazilian researcher.

"Hector," said Pedro, "We're going to stop for lunch now."

Hector was glad to climb down for lunch. He raised his insect net and dozens of tiny stingless bees, attracted by his sweat, crawled over his face.

"The female is sitting on eggs," he told Pedro and Veronica. Veronica was a visiting American student who was studying the breeding problems of macaws.

"Is this one of the best places for macaws to breed?" she asked.

"Yes, it is," said Hector. "There are plenty of large, old trees and no humans – except for us! In so many places the loggers have removed all the big, old trees. Unfortunately, macaws still don't seem to do very well here. A recent study of 100 nesting pairs of macaws in the park

A pair of blue-and-gold macaws at their nest hole. The female does not need to be camouflaged, because she cannot be seen by predators when she is in the hole.

showed that only 15 to 25 young were raised each year. Only a small number of the birds that live here seem to nest in any one year.

"These blue-and-gold macaws had a bad time last year. The female was driven out of her nest hole by another pair, and the male vanished. We think that he was

Macaws fly through the forest in small groups, calling noisily. You can hear them coming from a long way off.

killed. This year she has a new mate. Even where there are plenty of holes, only one or two pairs nest in every 3 to 4 square kilometres."

The Manu National Park consists of dense rainforest like that shown above. Rivers wind between the trees. The green canopy is broken here and there by an extra tall tree that pushes into the sunlight.

"There are seven species of macaws in this national park," said Hector proudly. "We are trying to find out how many of each kind there are, what they feed on, and how and where they find the food. We know that the scarlet macaws eat over 40 different kinds of nuts and fruits.

"We don't really know much about how macaws live in the wild. Some may even move to different parts of the forest at different times of the year. If we are to save them from extinction we need to learn much much more."

After lunch, the three researchers set off along the forest trail. They were following a rough map and looking for signs of macaws. Macaws waste a lot of their food. They like to take nuts back to a perch to eat, but often they drop them by mistake. The shells and husks of the nuts they do eat also fall to the ground. Nuts cracked by macaws have incredibly smooth, clean cuts. The outside of the shell often shows grooves where the bird has tried to grip it in its bill. This makes it easy to tell whether shells have been dropped by macaws or monkeys.

They were counting shells beneath a large nut tree when Veronica gave a cry. She had found the tracks of an ocelot.

Ocelots will stalk macaws when the birds are feeding on the ground. Danger also comes from the air; large forest eagles can easily seize a perching macaw.

Veronica knelt down and examined the seeds that they had found beneath the tree.

"Some of these are very poisonous," she remarked. "These are soapbox tree seeds, and there are some mahogany seeds."

"Macaws seem to be able to cope with the poisons," said Hector. "They also eat unripe fruit, which other birds and mammals cannot eat. This means that they can find food that no other animals want to eat."

"How can they eat poison?" asked Veronica.

"Macaws and other forest parrots

Each macaw has its own characteristic pattern of lines on its face. This is how researchers recognize individual birds.

regularly visit clay licks," replied Hector. "These are banks of clay that have been exposed by the river. The macaws swallow large chunks of clay. We think that the clay helps to absorb the poisons, or to make them harmless. The Indians of the Andes mix wild potatoes with clay to remove the poisons in them."

"I'd like to see the macaws on the clay," said Veronica.

"We'll go tomorrow morning," promised Hector.

At dawn the next day, they set out for the clay lick. It was a steep bank beside a gurgling stream. Pedro and Hector fired a rope over the branches of a tall tree nearby, and hauled up a rope ladder. This time it was Pedro's turn to keep watch above. He was to watch the birds flying in from other parts of the forest, and to record where each group came from.

Hector and Veronica settled down with notebooks. It was a good chance for Veronica to learn to recognize individual macaws and parrots.

Macaws and other forest parrots visit clay licks like the one shown here about three times a week.

Soon the researchers heard the sound of screeching. Small groups of parrots flew in and started squabbling over the best places on the bank. Clinging on with their claws, the parrots scraped chunks of clay into their mouths with their bills. A steady trickle of clay crumbs splashed into the stream. Soon the bank was thick with hundreds of colourful parrots. With them were a few species of medium-sized macaws. Chestnut-fronted macaws and red-bellied macaws were feeding side by side.

Pedro radioed down from his look-out post.

"Large macaws flying from the west – scarlets, I think," he said.

The large macaws began to arrive in twos and threes. At first they were cautious, sitting in nearby trees, preening nervously, screeching and squabbling. Eventually they, too, flew down to the bank.

Veronica and Hector were making notes and sketching the birds as quickly as they could.

All of a sudden, there was a lot of noise and flapping of wings, and the birds began flying away. A shadow flashed across the bank, and there was an anguished squawk. A harpy eagle had flown in and snatched a luckless parrot.

"Time to go," said Hector. "They won't come back now, as the sun is quite high."

Hector was eager to get back to the camp. He and Pedro were due to leave that afternoon to visit a research project in Brazil. They were hoping to see the rare hyacinth macaws.

Below: harpy eagles are fierce forest predators. With their powerful talons, they can easily capture macaws and even monkeys.

Above: scarlet macaws and red-and-green macaws on a clay lick in Peru. This area is home to seven species of macaws.

"Butia" palm trees in Brazil. Hyacinth macaws nest in clumps of palm trees in woodland lining the rivers, or in holes in nearby cliffs.

The following day, Hector and Pedro were in the grasslands of southeast Brazil, the home of the hyacinth macaw. Pedro led Hector to a small swampy area surrounded by palm trees.

"Is this where they nest?" asked Hector.

"It is," replied Pedro. "We'll probably find the macaws near the cattle. The cattle feed on palm nuts, and the macaws eat them, too."

As they approached the cattle, Pedro spotted a large, dark macaw sitting on a fence post. It was watching some others as they hunted for nuts on the ground.

The birds suddenly noticed the two men, and flew off, squawking loudly. Their brilliant purple plumage gleamed in the afternoon sun.

"Has the pet bird trade reduced their numbers?" asked Hector.

"Yes," replied Pedro. "Cattle ranchers are also moving their cattle into this area. Hyacinth macaws make very good pets. Not only are they extremely beautiful, but they are very easily tamed and very good-tempered. They are also good talkers.

"Of course, to get the best pets you have to get them used to humans while they are young. For this reason, the trappers try to take the young from the nests. Then this kind of thing happens."

Pedro showed Hector a palm tree that had recently been broken off, leaving a jagged stump.

"There was a nest with two young chicks in here before I went to Peru," he said. "Trappers must have cut the whole tree down. That's another nest site lost."

The hyacinth macaw is the largest species. Only about 3,000 remain in the wild because so many have been taken for the pet trade and for bird collectors.

"Can't you stop the trapping?" asked Hector.

"Well, it is already illegal," said Pedro. "Unfortunately, it makes the local people a lot of money. One of these birds can fetch up to £13,000 abroad. The trappers are paid very little money, but even that is more than they are paid for other kinds of work. Unfortunately, some smugglers don't look after their birds. For every macaw that arrives safely in another country, five probably die on the way."

Pedro took Hector to visit a local trapper, Felipe. Hector was dismayed to see the children's ragged clothes, the dirty streets and dark cramped shacks without water or electricity supplies. Felipe was grumbling about the broken tree.

"The people who damaged that tree weren't local people," he said. "We don't cut the trees down. It doesn't make sense. We want the birds to keep on nesting here. We just climb up and remove the chicks. Of course, we always leave one chick in the nest so that the parents will stay. If we didn't do that, there wouldn't be more birds for the future."

Felipe's wife, Conchita, was feeding some young macaw chicks with a spoon. Hector was relieved to see how much these trappers cared for the young birds. He knew,

A pair of hyacinth macaws at their nest. The trees that these macaws nest in disappear when cattle ranchers move in.

however, that many birds would die after they left the safety of Felipe's home.

"Have you any idea who cut down that tree?" Pedro asked.

"No," replied Felipe, "but a man and a boy have been asking for food and shelter in Salinas. That's the village in the next valley."

Pedro was angry.

"I'm going to track them down and fetch the police," he said firmly. "Once these people find a nesting area, they won't stop at just one visit."

Conchita fed the macaw chicks on a diet of gooey cereals, cornmeal and boiled rice.

THEFT IN THE JUNGLE

Carlos Lopez looked out glumly at the rain as it ran off the tin roofs and trickled down the street in a dirty stream. As far as he could see, grey skies stretched over Sao Paulo, the great sprawling city on the coast of Brazil. His family had come to this dreary shanty town a year ago.

Carlos looked around him at the litter, the mangy dog scavenging behind the shack, and the thin, pale children playing in the mud. He wished he was back in the forest. There the rain sang as it trickled through the trees and the birds answered it.

There were no birds here, not even his pet macaw, Coco. Coco had fled when the cattle ranchers had moved in with their guns and turned Carlos's family out of their home. The ranchers wanted their land to raise cattle. His family had come to Sao Paulo with just a few possessions.

Carlos's father had found work at the docks, but then he had become ill. Now they relied on the small amount of money Carlos's mother earned selling baskets.

It was a good thing Coco had not come with them. There was no food to spare, and no money to buy grain. Carlos hoped the bird had survived in the forest.

Tomorrow would be better. Uncle Emilio was coming.

Left: Carlos was unhappy. He missed the jungle, the singing birds and insects, the lush growth and bright flowers. He also missed collecting fruit and going fishing.

Above: the rainforest in Brazil. Here, Carlos's family had been able to grow all their own food and keep a cow for milk. In Sao Paulo, they had barely enough to eat.

Uncle Emilio's arrival made everyone happy. He had brought a big basket of fruit for Carlos's mother, and beer for his father. Emilio ran a small pet shop on the other side of Rio. Carlos loved to visit him and see all the animals, especially the parrots. They reminded him of Coco.

Uncle Emilio wanted to take Carlos on a trip back to the jungle. He was going to catch parrots for his shop, he said.

"Ordinary parrots, or special ones to sell?" asked Carlos's father. He knew that his brother sometimes sold rare parrots for large amounts of money to foreign dealers. The dealers would then smuggle the birds out of the country.

"Special ones," laughed Emilio. "I need Carlos's help because he is young and very good at climbing trees. I'll give him a share of the money we make."

Carlos was excited. It would be the first time he had seen the forest since they had left for the city. He also felt proud that he could earn some money for his family.

Uncle Emilio in his pet shop. Emilio caught macaws illegally and sold them to foreign dealers.

A hyacinth macaw bred in captivity. People should never buy macaws that have been taken from the wild. Birds bred in captivity make happier pets.

"What kind of birds are we collecting?" he asked.

"Hyacinth macaws," said Emilio.

"I've never seen those," said Carlos. "Were they in the forest?"

"There weren't any where you lived," explained Emilio. "They live in more open country. This visit won't be to proper rainforest, but to small patches of woodland and palm groves." Emilio showed Carlos a picture of the hyacinth macaws.

Three days later, Uncle Emilio and Carlos were camped in the grassland near Salinas.

23

Carlos and Emilio set out soon after dawn. Suddenly, a group of macaws flew past, shrieking loudly. Carlos had never seen such big ones. They looked almost black against the dawn sky.

"Wait until you see them in the sunshine," said Emilio. "They're magnificent."

Emilio led Carlos to a clump of palm trees. As they approached, a hyacinth macaw flew out of a tree, squawking angrily.

"That looks like a nest hole," said Emilio. "Why don't you climb up and have a look?"

Carlos began to climb the tree. When he was a short distance from the nest, the female bird flew out, giving him such a surprise that he lost his footing and fell out of the tree. Carlos grabbed at a branch, but it slowly bent under him, and he fell about five metres to the ground.

"I've hurt my ankle," he groaned, trying to stand.

Emilio strapped up Carlos's ankle with his scarf.

"Never mind," said Emilio. "We'll cut the tree down." He had brought a small chain-saw with him. The sound echoed across the landscape. Carlos was horrified as the tree crashed down.

"Won't it hurt the babies?" Carlos asked, as he felt gently in the hole for the chicks. To his relief, the first chick he brought out seemed all right. It was bobbing its head and chirping. The second chick wasn't all right. It was lying in a strange twisted position, quite still and lifeless.

"Let's go," said Emilio. "Someone may have heard the saw."

As Carlos reached the hole, the female macaw suddenly flew out. Carlos was so startled that he fell. Now they would cut down the tree.

An adult scarlet macaw and chicks at the nest hole. Female macaws feed their young on food that has been already partly digested.

Carlos and Emilio returned to their camp. Carlos had brought some grain for the birds, but he had not expected such a tiny chick.

"It's got hardly any feathers," he said. "Do you think it will survive?" It can't eat this grain. It needs something softer."

"We'd better buy some rice and cereal then," said Emilio.

They set off for Salinas. Carlos was still carrying the chick, hidden under a cloth in his basket. As they were looking in the window of the village shop, Carlos noticed two young men watching them closely. He nudged his uncle. Emilio went inside the shop and quickly bought some grain. The two men moved

even closer. It was Hector and Pedro. Just at that moment, the chick started chirping.

"What's that noise?" Pedro asked Carlos, although he already knew.

Carlos slowly lifted the cloth.

"Come on," said Emilio, urgently, "We have to go."

Emilio started to walk away. At that moment, the local policeman arrived. He had come to arrest Emilio. The policeman searched Emilio's bag, and found the saw, with fragments of palm leaves still clinging to it. The policeman told Emilio that he had to go to the police house and the two men turned to walk away.

"I can't jail the boy – he's too young," said the policeman.

"We'll take Carlos back to our village," said Pedro. "Felipe and Conchita will look after him."

Soon, Felipe and Conchita were showing Carlos how to make a proper meal for his chick.

A young Jivaro Indian wearing a ceremonial headdress made from the feathers of macaws and parrots. His people have hunted macaws for their feathers for centuries.

"Do you realize that this chick will probably die," said Pedro, sternly, "even if it survives the trip to Sao Paulo?"

Carlos looked up miserably.

"In a few years' time," Pedro went on, "there won't be any more hyacinth macaws left because so many have been taken to sell. Some other kinds of macaws have already become extinct."

Carlos was shocked to think that such beautiful birds might

Hahn's macaws, bred and kept in captivity. If enough birds are kept for breeding instead of being sold as pets, there would be no need to sell wild birds to anyone.

disappear for ever.

"Then I'll keep this one," he said. "If Uncle Emilio is in jail, he can't stop me. I won't let it die."

Felipe watched the boy gently feeding the chick. He could see that Carlos cared for the chick.

"You can stay here with us for as long as you like," Felipe said. "We'll show you how to feed the chick and look after it properly."

Hector and Pedro strolled home.

"Why don't you put the police on to Felipe?" asked Hector.

"I need to do my research here," said Pedro, "I don't want to upset the local people. At least they are careful not to take too many birds, or to damage their nest holes. It is better to teach the local people to care about the birds. Perhaps one day tourists from other countries will want to come and see the birds. That would bring money into the area, and people wouldn't need to sell the macaws."

Wild hyacinth macaws face many threats. Their nest trees are destroyed by ranchers, and they are hunted for food and feathers and for the pet trade.

FOR LOVE OF MACAWS

"Pepe eat! Pepe eat! Come and get it!" called the macaw.

Arthur Copland picked up some nuts and seeds and held out his hand. Pepe, a large scarlet macaw, landed on his shoulder, and nuzzled Arthur gently. Then Pepe bent down to look at her breakfast. Ignoring all the colourful seeds, she chose the largest brazil nut and flapped back to her perch, making small noises of delight.

Pepe and Arthur were good friends. Pet macaws need a great deal of attention. They often form long-lasting relationships with humans.

Pepe held the nut firmly in her foot, and pressed on the seam of the shell with the points of her beak. Then she carefully put it between her two bills, or mandibles, and gripped it firmly. There was a loud crack, and Pepe used her tongue to take the kernel of the nut from its shell.

Pepe had been Arthur's main companion since his wife had died forty years ago. The parrot had been wrongly named. One of

Scarlet macaws preening each other. This keeps the feathers clean, as it removes parasites and the bases of dead feathers which cause disease.

Arthur's bird-breeder friends had offered to find out the bird's sex, and they had discovered that Pepe was really a female! The bird was now at least 45 years old. Pepe had won many prizes for Arthur in bird shows, but these days Arthur left her at home.

Scarlet macaws in flight. This species is common in captivity but endangered in the wild.

Some days later, Arthur was at a local bird show when his friend, Bill Baker, walked in with another man.

"Arthur," said Bill, "meet Clifford Sykes, chief keeper at the Parrot Park." The Parrot Park was a bird zoo that specialized in breeding parrots and macaws.

"I've been wanting to meet you," said Clifford, eagerly. "I'm told you have a female scarlet macaw. We were wondering if you would be willing to lend her to us to see if we can breed by her. There is a great shortage of female scarlet macaws."

Arthur didn't much like the idea.

"I'm not sure about that," Arthur said slowly. "Pepe has been with me for so long. I'd be lost without her! I'm not sure she would settle anywhere else."

"Did you realize that the scarlet macaw is now an endangered species?" Clifford asked.

"I had no idea," said Arthur. "I thought they were quite common."

"They are common in captivity," said Clifford, "but the rainforest is being cut down so quickly, and many macaws are being captured for the pet bird trade.

"In many parts of South and Central America they are already extinct. That's why we need to breed them here. We need to build up a large number of birds in captivity in case the wild birds disappear completely. If we can also provide enough birds for the pet trade, maybe we can persuade people not to buy birds that have been caught in the wild. We still have a lot of work to do in that area."

Macaws are sociable birds. It is not kind to keep them alone. Macaw pairs are very affectionate.

Arthur wanted to help, but he just couldn't bring himself to part with Pepe.

"Perhaps you'd like to come up to the Parrot Park one day," suggested Clifford, "and see our breeding birds."

When Arthur got back home, he was greeted by welcoming squawk. "Hello Arthur! Tea now!" said the bird. As Arthur boiled the kettle, Pepe suddenly began to squawk an alarm. There was someone at the front door.

Arthur peered through the window to see who the visitor was. The face seemed familiar, and then Arthur realized it was a man who had been standing near him while he was talking to Clifford and Bill. He opened the door cautiously.

"Good afternoon," said the stranger. "I'm Trevor Hughes. I'm a bird dealer, and I'd very much like to buy your macaw."

"How did you know I had one?" asked Arthur.

"I could hear it from the road," said the man. Arthur thought it was more likely that the man had overheard his earlier conversation with Clifford.

"Sorry," said Arthur, firmly. "The bird is not for sale." He accompanied the stranger to the gate to make sure that he didn't hang around.

Arthur was afraid that the stranger might attempt to steal Pepe. Macaws are often stolen because they are valuable.

The scarlet macaw has recently been declared endangered. In many countries, it is against the law to send the birds to another country or to receive them. This means that there will soon be a shortage of scarlet macaws in some countries. When this happens they will become expensive. Anyone who owns a scarlet macaw will be able to make a lot of money.

Right: an illegal bird market. Below: a bird market in Hong Kong. Hundreds of thousands of birds are sold every year. It is still cheaper to obtain birds from the wild than to breed them in captivity.

After the parrot show, Clifford Sykes had gone to a conference in the Philippines. While he was there he went to see a bird dealer who had two Spix's macaws. The Spix's macaw is perhaps the rarest of all macaws. There is probably only one bird left in the wild, and about 25 in captivity, most of them old.

It is difficult to find out where the birds are. Spix's macaws have been protected by law for so long that almost all the privately owned birds have been caught illegally. The only hope for saving this species is to breed them in captivity. Then, one day, some of them can be taken back to the wild, if a safe enough place can be found.

A Lear's or indigo macaw. There have never been many of this species. They have lost much of their habitat, and too many have been collected for the trade in caged birds.

Clifford wanted to borrow the birds to try to breed them. The man did not want to part with them.

"They won't breed," he said. "I've had them for years."

"Perhaps," said Clifford, "they are both the same sex. Do you know if they are male or female?"

"No," said the dealer, firmly. "The operation that they use to find out is too risky. I'm not going to have that done to birds as valuable as these."

"There is a new method being developed," said Clifford. "They take one of the feather sheaths and test that. It's quite safe."

"No thanks," said the dealer. "If you want to buy the birds, I'll accept £20,000 each."

"We don't have the funds," said Clifford, angrily.

Clifford returned to England. He was angry with the dealer for being so greedy. The dealer knew that the fewer Spix's macaws there were, the more valuable his would become. He wasn't interested in helping a breeding programme.

A pair of Spix's macaws, the rarest of all macaws. There is only one left in the wild. Captive birds are very valuable.

Arthur came to see Clifford at the Parrot Park as planned. Many of the macaws were flying outside in a very large aviary.

"These birds usually breed at this time of year." explained Clifford. "Although macaws pair for life, they can be quite choosy about their mates, and they breed best with a partner they really like. So we give them the chance to meet up and choose."

"That's an odd pair," remarked Arthur, pointing to two macaws of different colour preening each other.

"Yes," said Clifford. "That's a male scarlet macaw and a female blue-and-gold macaw. The male looks as if he may mate with her. See how his cheeks are blushing? They will produce hybrid young, a mixture of the two colour patterns. We don't encourage breeding hybrids. We would prefer the birds to produce more of their own species. Hybrids are popular in the USA, but not in Europe. We were hoping Pepe might be a better mate for him."

On a table Arthur saw a pile of brilliant feathers.

"We save the feathers when they drop out," said Clifford. "We send them to Central America. The local people use them in ceremonial dances. A lot of macaws are killed for their feathers. By sending the feathers so they can be sold or rented, we hope to prevent the wild birds being killed."

Clifford and Arthur moved into the breeding section of the zoo. In one room, baby macaws were being reared by hand.

Sometimes different species of macaws can breed together in captivity to produce hybrid young.

Arthur was fascinated by the tiny macaws. Some had hardly any feathers, while some had a few spiky adult feathers just beginning to show.

"What kind are these?" he asked.

"Military macaws," replied Clifford. "That one's about six weeks old."

"There's a sick one," said Arthur, pointing to one of the chicks.

"No, it's not," laughed Clifford. "That one's just had a big meal. The lump that you can see is its crop, a throat pouch for storing food. Digestion takes a while because seeds are very hard. The macaw also has a muscular gizzard. This sometimes contains grit, which helps to break down the seeds."

A blue-fronted macaw in a zoo. Macaws reared in captivity are calmer and more affectionate than those from the wild.

"Macaws breed very slowly," said Clifford. "They produce only two eggs a year, and those do not always hatch. If we remove the eggs and rear the young birds ourselves, the adults will usually lay again the same year. That way we get twice as many eggs. Also, the birds we rear ourselves are more likely to survive than the others."

In the next room were some macaws with chicks.

"We always let the birds raise some of their own chicks," said Clifford. "After all, one day we may want to reintroduce them to the wild, and they need to have the experience. We've found that it also makes them happier."

"Is it true that birds bred in captivity are more healthy than wild ones?" asked Arthur.

"Usually," said Clifford. "Wild birds often have diseases and parasites. Birds that are caught for the pet trade also catch diseases from other birds while they are being moved between countries."

Baby chicks are helpless at birth, and have only a few fluffy feathers. From left to right, the picture below shows chicks at 8-9 weeks, 4 weeks, 6 weeks and at 11-12 weeks.

"Do you ever sell any of these young birds as pets?" asked Arthur.

" Very seldom," replied Clifford. "We keep most of them so that we can build up a good large captive population. In any case, macaws are not really very suitable as pets. They are sociable birds, and if they are kept alone they can become very bad-tempered. They can give a nasty bite and their claws are very sharp, too. They need at least two hours of human attention a day for them to be happy. They're also very noisy.

"Macaws can live as long as humans, but they don't live as long in captivity as they do in the wild. This is because the stress makes them more likely to catch diseases.

"I wonder if Pepe is stressed," said Arthur.

"How long have you had her?" asked Clifford.

"Forty years," said Arthur. "I travelled to South America on a cargo ship, and I bought her in a market. She was being so badly treated by the man who owned her that I just had to rescue her!"

"In that case," said Clifford, "she must be well over forty years old. I don't even know if she will breed at that age, but it would certainly upset her to move. It would be best if you keep her."

Arthur returned home to the usual warm welcome from Pepe. He tickled the bird's head affectionately. He had never realized that he had taken the place of a lifelong mate for Pepe, just as Pepe had helped to comfort him over the loss of his wife all those years ago.

Left: Arthur returned to Pepe. Pepe, like all macaws, was very intelligent and easily bored. People should be aware of this before deciding to buy a macaw or a parrot for a pet.

Above: a military macaw in its natural home, the mountain forest of South America. If it is to survive, the forest must be preserved and the illegal trade in wild birds must be stopped.

MACAW
UPDATE

Macaws are large, very intelligent parrots that live in rainforests and other wooded areas of tropical and subtropical South and Central America. There are 16 different species. The number of macaws in the wild is falling drastically. The main threats are the destruction of their forest habitats, and capture for the trade in captive birds to supply pet shops and private collectors. This is happening even though the capture and export of wild macaws is illegal in many countries. Many trapped macaws die before they reach their destination. As a species becomes rarer, it is bought and sold illegally for large sums of money. As its value increases, more birds are stolen from the wild.

Blue-and-Gold Macaw ● This species is up to 90 centimetres long, and has a very long tail. It is quite common in lowland South America and Panama, specially in riverside forests and palm swamps. It has suffered from habitat loss, and large numbers have been trapped for the bird trade. It breeds well in captivity.

Chestnut-Fronted Macaw ● This species is sometimes called the severe macaw and is only about 49 centimetres long. It is still quite common in open lowland forests throughout northern South America, but it has disappeared from many areas recently. It is rare in captivity.

Hyacinth Macaw ● This is the largest species and grows up to 100 centimetres long. It lives in riverside forests and palm swamps of southern Brazil, eastern Bolivia and northeastern Paraguay. It is uncommon and very valuable. There are only a few in captivity. The main threat has been trapping for the bird trade.

Blue-and-gold macaw

Chestnut-fronted macaw

Hyacinth macaw

Lear's Macaw ● This species grows to a length of about 75 centimetres. It is found in canyon country with thorn scrub and clumps of palms in northeastern Brazil. There have never been many Lear's macaws. Today there may be only about 20 birds left. Its habitat is being destroyed by cattle ranchers.

Lear's
macaw

Red-Bellied Macaw ● This species is only 46 centimetres long. It is found in palm swamps in northern South America. Its survival will depend on the survival of the palm swamps. It is very nervous, and does not breed easily in captivity.

Spix's macaw

Red-bellied macaw

Red-and-green
macaw

Scarlet macaw

Military macaw

Red-and-Green Macaw ● Sometimes known as the green-winged macaw, this species grows up to 90 centimetres long. It is found in many lowland forests in tropical and subtropical Central and South America, but its forest home is being destroyed. Only a few have bred in captivity.

Spix's Macaw ● This species grows to a length of only 55 centimetres. It is found in palm groves in northeastern Brazil. It was probably never very numerous, but because of trapping for the bird trade it is now extremely rare. There may be only one bird left in the wild and about 25 in captivity worldwide.

Scarlet Macaw ● This species grows up to 90 centimetres long. It is widespread in the lowlands of South and Central America, where it prefers to live in open woodland, trees along rivers, grasslands and plantations. It is threatened by destruction of its habitat, illegal trapping for the pet trade and killing for its feathers. It breeds well in captivity.

Military Macaw ● This species grows to about 75 centimetres long. It is found in the mountain forests of Central and South America. It is threatened by habitat destruction, illegal trapping for the bird trade, and killing for the feather trade. Its numbers are declining seriously, but it is fairly common in captivity in the USA, although there is little captive breeding.

INDEX